OVERCOME YOUR BIOLOGY, MEET YOUR ORIGINAL SELF, AND LIVE THE LIFE YOU ARE DESTINED FOR

SHAKANNA LAUER

With love,

(signature)

For more information, email tandemhealthmbs@gmail.com

Get your free guide!

To get the best experience with this book, I've found readers who download and use the *"Beginner's Guide to Self Care"* are able to implement faster and take the next steps needed to create a healthy and soulful life.

You can get a copy by visiting:
https://www.tandemhealth.online/freedownload

In dedication to:

My mother and father, Melinda and Donald Inman,
who taught me to love, and
instilled in me the belief that life is beautiful.

My husband, Henry Lauer, for carrying me when I
haven't the strength, and for
always encouraging my endeavors.

Table of contents

Introduction

I

I'd like to start by saying that this is a book where the concept of humans having a soul is a fact. However, the steps in the book can still help you, even if you don't believe this. This is where science meets the soul—where we can overcome our biological and social conditioning and create any life we want.

If you desire a life of joy and happiness, it will come to you, but you have to do the work of uncovering that which holds you back from living this envisioned life. You have to be patient; you must have love for yourself. You need to conjure a belief that you are worthy of this envisioned life and hold on to it—it will be your guiding light. If you weren't worthy, you wouldn't be here.

This book will help you uncover what has prevented you from flourishing into your desired life and will help you move beyond those limiting beliefs so you can begin taking steps toward what you desire. It will also give you vital information and tools to cultivate a healthy lifestyle with daily habits that will help you be your best self. Doing the work of understanding and releasing your limiting beliefs, as well as using healthy habits to become the best version of yourself, will lead you to your desired life—one that speaks to your soul.

To get what you want, you have to know what you want. To know what you want, you have to know your authentic self; no other version of you will suffice. The pages of this book will take you through the steps of getting back to basics and clearing out all that no longer serves you so you can let your authentic self come to life.

So. Let's get back to basics—our biology. In the following chapters, we'll discuss the fundamental systems which drive the biological aspect of our wellbeing. Those biological systems begin with the mind and nervous system, then branch out to bodily systems and what is necessary for their proper function, including hydration, pre-biotics, pro-biotics, and other organ systems such as our digestive, circulatory, and lymphatic systems. Throughout each section, I will explain these systems, what they require, how they work, and why they are vital to our wellbeing.

This book is a tool you will use in your journey to overcoming limiting beliefs that stem from learned behaviors and social conditioning. It will also teach you how to build healthy habits to help your body get back to ground zero so that you can cultivate harmony within yourself.

This is a step-by-step guide on how to realize your full potential. The power to do this is in your hands, literally. Whatever outcome you desire can be yours if you let it, but you must commit to the changes you wish to see.

I will share my number one tool for realizing your full potential in life. It's the most overlooked step to overcoming any obstacle and the key that makes it all work. Are you ready to build healthy habits that last, discover who you truly are, and make space for yourself to thrive? If so, read on. This book is a crash course for making your dreams come true.

Part One explores and explains the scientific aspects of our mind and body wellbeing, while Part Two covers wellbeing for our soul. I will show you a snapshot of mind-body-soul wellbeing and offer vital information for your success, but in order for you to succeed, you must do the work.

By the end of this book, you will have reconnected with your authentic self—your inner child. Through unraveling the layers of your persona, you will begin to understand how you became disconnected from this essential version of you and how you can befriend and use this authentic self to reach your full potential.

However, to thrive in your full potential, you must first create harmony within your physical self. This is essentially getting back to the basics of what your mental and physical selves need. Your physical wellbeing must come before your soul's wellbeing. This is the natural order of things—our hierarchy of needs. Before we dive into the details on how to do all this, let me tell a bit about myself and how I came to write this book.

II

I still remember the way the soft, cool dirt felt under my bare feet. The earth cushioned each step beneath me. The smell of sweet sap filled the air in early spring as trees began to bud, and soon bright pink salmonberry flowers filled the undergrowth as far as I could see. Birds sang their sweet melodies, and water trickled across rocks in the creek. It was heaven on earth, our own little paradise away from the world.

I walked step by step beside my mother as she taught me about earth's bounty. We spotted the perfect place to plant our flowers and built teepees out of fallen branches. At night we sat around a campfire playing music and telling stories, sending notes to our Spirit Guides up in flames as prayers. This was my early childhood.

Many years later, when starting my own journey toward a life that truly spoke to me, I realized this is what I was looking for—my inner peace. It took a long time before I realized that embracing this inward reflection of my lost childhood was a necessary step in breaking out of my vicious cycles of depression and anxiety.

I chose to go back and unravel every trauma and every repeated lesson until I had untangled my entire life. I made this choice to thoroughly understand what I wanted as an adult and how my younger self ended up with such limiting beliefs and self-sabotaging behaviors. I wanted, more than anything, to have passion, love, and joy back in my life. I wanted to move past hurt and heartache, to get to a place where I could be myself again—my true, authentic self.

I had to shed layers and layers of self-doubt, expectations, judgment, hypocrisy, and toxicity that had formed over years of trauma and disappointment. I was not satisfied with a life that was anything less than what it was meant to be, so I held tight to a belief that life is beautiful. Eventually, all of my bottled-up negativity disappeared; resentment, anger, sadness, and grief all left. There was no room for that which did not bring beauty and peace into my life.

You might be wondering what happened after my early childhood that brought my desperation for inner peace. Although my early years were beautiful and full of magic, I was destined to live the rest of my childhood and early adult years in turmoil.

I suppose my father's passing was the first indication that I might have a rough road ahead of me. He died from cancer when I was nine. His wish was to forego all Western treatment—no chemo, radiation, morphine, or anything of the sort. This wish led to moving the family to Mexico, where he pursued treatment, and Mom homeschooled me.

We left at the end of December 2002, and he died in March 2003, three days after his 60th birthday. My dad and mom were at the hospital, and they'd left me home. One morning I remember our friend driving me to the hospital; I saw my mother sitting on the bench outside, face in hands, sobbing. I knew. We got to my mom, and she told us he died in the night. Then she took us back to see him to say goodbye. All colors of life had left him. What remained was cold and grey. Lifeless. That wasn't my dad.

It was tough; I was young and didn't fully understand the gravity of what it meant when someone died—not to mention it being my father. My mother was a wreck, too, so I felt I needed to be strong for her. I needed her to know that I was okay. But the truth was, I wasn't.

I bottled up the emotions I didn't understand and pretended that nothing happened; I believed that life would go on as it always had. I never spoke to my mother, or anyone, about what happened. And no one asked if I wanted to—or needed to.

Needless to say, life didn't return to normal. I hardly saw or spoke to my mother for the next year of my life; she became so overwhelmed with her grief that she disconnected from reality. She told me years later that she had made plans for my brothers to take custody of me so that she could drown herself in the river to be with my dad again. Luckily, she sought help and recovered—as much as a person can recover from losing the love of their life.

Her recovery brought her back to reality, but she was still very much a broken soul. She had been broken since her childhood, after a traumatic upbringing and multiple abusive relationships. When she finally met my father, he lifted her up, and together they created the beautiful life I remember from my childhood.

However, after he died, a piece of her died with him. Eventually, she put herself together as best she could, and one full year after losing my dad, she met her next partner, who I refer to as my step-dad. He was also a broken soul.

This time my mother tried to raise him up, the way my dad helped her. Unfortunately, my mom and step-dad both suffered from mental illness and chose not to seek help. Caught in the throes of alcohol addiction and bipolar disorder, to name a few, their unhealed traumas haunted them.

I was in the transition between middle school and high school when reality began to sink in, and at that point, my life became very dark. Darkness remained with me for many years. You see, being a teenager with two alcoholic parents unsuccessfully struggling with their own trauma leaves a lasting impact on your life. I vividly remember the fighting, yelling, name-calling, spitting, all of which were followed by days of unrelenting silence—a loud silence filled with hurt and perceived hatred. Never have I felt so fragile in all my life.

Looking back, I now know that the way I was treated was not of my own doing. I did nothing to bring forth the hurtful words or emotional abuse. Nonetheless, the effects of this mistreatment crept into my psyche, where it roiled for years, torturing me. The worst part was how much I longed for a father again, and that role was filled by someone who was not always ready for the task. As many times as he tried to leave, I would beg him to stay. "Don't leave me, Daddy," I would cry in the middle of the night while they fought. I needed help, but so did they.

Love is a powerful thing, as is fear and hate. It was my mother's love for my father and me which kept her alive. Her love for me also brought light into my darkness, as did the love of my step-dad. Despite his flaws and harsher than preferred parenting techniques, he did everything he could to see me thrive. Their support and consistent pushing kept me from spiraling out of control. It was my will to live a beautiful life that drove me to rise out of the depths of darkness into which I fell at the young age of nine, after my father's death.

I navigated life's transitions from my father's death to my mother's battle with cancer, which she quickly lost when I was twenty-one, to my own fight with chronic pain and disease The skills and mental clarity I developed from having to work through these hardships on my own have proven useful time and time again. Now I am ready to pass on what I have learned and what has helped me realize my limitless potential. You, too, can live a beautiful, peaceful, joyful life.

– Part One –

OVERCOMING OUR BIOLOGY WITH THE SCIENCE OF WELLBEING

– Chapter 1 –

Our Nervous System and the Fear Mindset

The Main Lesson

To start this journey, we will first look at the mind and how it works with our body. Our mind can also be considered our *emotional self,* which is a crucial aspect to our understanding of mental health. Our mind is governed by our thoughts, which can be ruled by emotion if we are not careful. Thus, a large part of cultivating a healthy mind is to be aware of our emotions, as well as the circumstances in our life which cause them.

Honestly, this could be an entire book on its own, and probably already is, so I am going to focus on only the information necessary for understanding how and why our body responds to some circumstances as perceived threats. I will also share why techniques such as meditation and breathwork are useful tools for working on the health of your mind. It will be up to you to further your education on this subject, should you desire a deeper understanding than what I offer here.

This section explains the relationship between our mind and our nervous system, as well as how our biological evolution needs to catch up to scientific and social advancements. The internet, telecommunication, and a fast-paced lifestyle have created an environment with much more social interaction than that which our ancestors experienced. Social interactions and life circumstances are both precursors to emotional response.

Often today, we primarily make life decisions based on being liked or accepted. This is because, on a biological level, we perceive that our survival is dependent on being part of society. Therefore, on this level, we feel threatened or upset when we don't receive approval or acceptance from others. This is largely an emotional response, and we then subconsciously rely on the same biological mechanisms that our ancestors used for surviving threats but for non-life-threatening social situations instead. This comes from our fight or flight response.

Luckily, we can upgrade our biology and enhance our evolution by practicing meditation and mindfulness in our day-to-day lives. When we use these practices to rewire our brains, we teach our minds how to allow emotions to flow through us instead of holding on to them. In turn, we then overcome our outdated biologic responses so we can move through life in a healthy, balanced way.

Overcoming our biology permits us to step out of stress and into a new way of creating our lives. We are no longer driven by our emotions and biological threat response but rather by what we *want* our lives to look like. When we achieve this on a generational scale, our species will adapt to have greater resilience to what it perceives as stressful or threatening. You *can* overcome innate biological responses and reactions to create a better life.

These ideas are not groundbreaking, and I am not the first to suggest that mindfulness may help an overstimulated nervous system. In fact, the information on this topic is so enormously vast that you can easily get lost down the rabbit hole of neuroscience, transcendentalism, and everything in between. Countless studies and experts on these topics are available; thus, I'll narrow this conversation to only the most pertinent information, so we don't fall into Wonderland.

Let's look at meditation and mindfulness for a moment. Consider this question: "What is mindfulness?" To be mindful means to be aware of your thoughts. If left to their own devices, our thoughts will run rampant. We think without thinking, and this often leads to a tangled mess in our minds. Do you ever have the same thought circling around in your mind, over and over? Is this helpful? Usually not. Do you get distracted throughout the day or feel on edge, but you're not sure why? Also not very helpful.

To stop these circulating thoughts, we must be conscious of what and how we are telling our brain to think, and mindfulness is a way of doing so. We must be mindful of our thoughts because being mindful helps focus on the present and calms this rampant babbling; it calms and slows down the nervous system.

Meditation and mindfulness vary in modality, and resources for learning these techniques are abundant. You are but an internet search or app away! In Chapter Five, I will share wisdom and techniques which were passed down to me from my mother and father. I owe them my peace, and I hope that you, too, can use this knowledge to find a sense of calm stability.

It is important to understand that our thoughts—whether or not we are aware of them—affect our nervous system, thus affecting our body and its ability to function properly. Understanding the biology behind our thinking, as well as the evolution of our social environment and how we respond to it, will give us more autonomy over the health of our mind in day-to-day life. Understanding the basis of how our minds respond to our environment is immensely helpful in overcoming these outdated biological responses because now we don't *have* to fight.

When we begin to feel a threat response, we have the capacity to turn it off and walk away from the situation. This helps to keep the nervous system in a state of calm, allowing for healing.

The nervous system is essentially a network with inputs and outputs. It uses the spine as a highway to transmit data to and from the brain. The nervous system reaches every part of our body, and it tells our brain how to operate our physical body based on external data. In other words, we are a biological computer.

We can break this network of nerves down into two key pieces—the central nervous system (CNS) and the peripheral nervous system (PNS). Consider the CNS as the structural aspect of our nervous system, brain, and spinal cord. This is the highway mentioned previously. The PNS is everything that lives outside the cranial cavity or spinal canal, essentially all the nerves throughout our body.

Our PNS splits into two different functions. One branch includes the somatic or voluntary functions, which allow us to consciously respond to environmental stimuli. The other branch includes autonomic functions, over which we don't have conscious control; this branch is otherwise known as the autonomic nervous system (ANS).

Our somatic system sends sensory and motor data between the CNS and PNS, and the nerves responsible for this data live primarily in the skin, joints, and muscles. Our

ANS controls nerves in our organs, blood vessels, and glands.

In other words, the somatic or voluntary system is for our external inputs and senses, while the autonomic is more for internal sensors, monitoring the balance of our automatic functions—breathing, heart rate, digestion, and so on. The ANS performs two other functions as well—fight or flight and rest and digest. These functions are referred to as the sympathetic and parasympathetic nervous systems, respectively.

So, we have the *structural* CNS and the *functional* PNS. Remember, our PNS splits into two branches: one operates voluntary responses, and the other operates our automatic responses. Our automatic responses control functions for fight or flight and rest and digest. Did you realize that fight or flight and rest and digest responses are automatic and not voluntary? Now that I've given you a *very* brief explanation of our nervous system and how it functions, I'll show you how this applies to mental health and living a life you truly love.

If you take *one* thing away from this chapter, I want it to be this—your mind responds to external information and sends your body signals for either a fight-or-flight response or a rest and digest response. Although it seems you have no control over this, you actually do.

Historically, humans evolved and thrived by relying on these responses to tell us when we were safe or in danger. These days we try to use the same method of deciphering our environment, but we are not aware that we're sending too much chaotic information to our minds. Thus, we often send information that gets interpreted inaccurately, which results in an inappropriate response.

Sensory overload is a prime example, but we can also look at almost any stressful non-life-threatening situation —traffic jams, supermarkets, public speaking, the list goes on. Sometimes it feels as though being alive in general is a threat to our survival. Odd, isn't it? That sometimes, we allow in so much stress that life itself begins to feel like a threat. This is what I refer to as the "living to survive" mentality. No matter the cause of stress, our body responds based on how we've evolved. This is not a problem.

The problem comes when the response hinders us instead of helps us. In other words, when we have a fight-or-flight response when we are not in danger. Over time, the cumulative effects of being stuck in a fight-or-flight loop have severe adverse health effects. Thus, the living to survive mentality is causing more harm than good.

If you desire a more balanced life filled with happiness and confidence, please overcome your biology and step out of the fear mindset so you can stop living just to survive.

You can begin to see life with clarity but doing so requires a unique approach for every single person because we all experience different stressful situations and have different tolerances to stress. What is important is identifying when you are in stressful situations. Identification requires awareness, which is a skill that must be learned. Once you are aware of your thoughts and emotions, you can trick your brain by using meditation and breathwork. Over time, your brain will rewire itself and forget that you are threatened—you will no longer be living in fight or flight, living to survive.

As I mentioned previously, our nervous system and survival mechanisms haven't evolved as fast as science and technology. Because of this, we often have inappropriate reactions and responses to our environment. When this happens often enough or is ongoing, we end up wiring our brains and teaching our nervous system that this is how we need to handle life. Traffic jam? Better have a heart attack. Someone bumped into me at the store? I should probably fight them.

It's time to overhaul these survival mechanisms and to reprogram our nervous system. One way to think of it is that we need to move away from *survival mechanisms* and move towards *social mechanisms,* like setting boundaries with ourselves and others.

Now that we have explored how the nervous system is structured and how it operates, as well as how our antiquated survival mechanisms are causing us more harm than good, I will give you a step-by-step process for how to approach your life based on nervous system health. Then you can restructure it in a way that will help you overcome your biology to move towards your higher purpose and the life you desire. To do this, you must master fear and your emotions around fear.

Fear brings stress, and chronic stress kills. Literally. For many people, our antiquated biological stress response is causing severe mental and physical illness. However, you can start to change this *right now*. In addition to learning stress management techniques such as meditation and mindfulness, try approaching any stressful situation in your life in this series of steps—identify, simplify, compromise, boundaries.

Identify

The first and most important step is that you *identify*. Become aware of the situation at hand. Many aspects of our lives can bring stress. It can be hard enough to be aware of these situations, let alone be aware of how they affect us, so this takes some introspective work on your part. I urge you to try this in *any* situation, no matter how big or small it seems to you—household chores, shopping, social outings, work, etcetera. Stressful situations can be activated by feelings of obligation, responsibility, fear of judgment, or fear of failure, to name a few. By identifying when you experience stress in your life, you are taking the first step in remedying how it affects your life. You're also deciding how to work with and through these feelings of obligation, responsibility, and fear. You are learning how to process your emotions.

Sometimes obligation and responsibility are self-imposed, while at other times, they can be requirements put on us by outside forces, such as work and life commitments. Regardless of the circumstances, it's essential to uncover the root cause of your response to the stress. If you don't give yourself some perspective of where the problem manifests, you won't enact change. What aspects of your life stress you out?

Simplify

After identifying stress-causing situations in your life, the next step is to look critically at each situation, exploring what it is about those circumstances that bring forth your distress.

You must simplify the situation. Simmer it down to the root cause. Stress is an emotional fight-or-flight response, which is a survival mechanism. What happened to you that caused you to build a survival mechanism around this type of situation? When you look closely, you may find that sometimes you think you are reacting to a problem at face value when you are actually responding to an entirely different stimulus altogether. Is your work stressing you out, or is it your coworker? Is your coworker stressing you out, or is it the way she speaks to you or treats you? Is it the way she speaks to you or how you interpret what she says? Are you perhaps misinterpreting the intent behind her words? Even if your coworker is being negative, rude, or what you suspect, do you need to participate in her behavior? Or perhaps the idea of going to the grocery store makes you anxious. Is it being in an unfamiliar environment that makes you nervous? Being around strangers? Their potential judgment?

Simplifying the situation makes the task at hand much more manageable. It allows us to overcome inappropriate responses to life and frees up our mental capacity for doing what we want instead of solely feeling like we are surviving. This form of analysis gives us a clearer picture of how to move forward, and in moving forward, we naturally get to our next step, which is understanding the compromises involved.

Compromise

Life is full of compromises, and part of being happy means understanding what you can and cannot compromise.

You don't always have the luxury of stepping out of a stressful situation, but it is crucial that, at some level, you say no to things that aren't good for you. This can be tricky to do, and it is up to you to determine what scope is appropriate. You can choose to disengage without completely discontinuing the relationship or situation. For example, work might be stressful, but you need to make money to support yourself and perhaps your family. Perhaps a particular relationship has brought you negativity, but you value this person and believe you are still better off with him or her in your life.

Yes, life is full of compromises, but we must understand what we are and are not willing to compromise. It is also vital to know that compromises can be temporary. You can always strive to improve your situation and only need to compromise for as long as you deem appropriate. It just so happens that to reach that point of stepping out of stress, we have to allow ourselves to be okay with the current situation. This is our compromise—tolerate the situation long enough to get out of it.

If you cannot tolerate your compromise any longer... Get. Out. Now. Make the change you know you need. Your wellbeing depends on it.

Boundaries

Once you understand the depth of compromise, you will set boundaries to enforce your will to achieve your desired outcome.

Setting and adhering to boundaries is vital to living the life you want. It puts you into the mindset that your desired life is necessary. For example, setting boundaries around behavior for a child shows them what is necessary for social interaction and what is appropriate or not. Setting boundaries and sticking with them shows you, and everyone else, what you need more or less of in your life and that you are serious about committing to positive change.

Setting boundaries around stressful yet unavoidable situations is imperative for your ability to move toward the life you desire. Decide what your compromise is, and then make it work. Is your health suffering from working a job that is not suited to you? What is your desired outcome, and what will you compromise to get there? How will you hold yourself to that? In this example, you may need to find a job that is a better fit for you, which means you may take a pay cut, must commute farther, or work different hours. The boundary associated with this example could be around friends, family, peers, your time, or any number of factors. Or maybe you need a higher-paying job, so you need to compromise your time and comfort zone and begin applying and interviewing for other work opportunities. Again, the boundary you need to set depends on where your stress is really coming from.

One more example of setting boundaries in stressful situations is setting a boundary around what you choose to participate in, energetically speaking. Perhaps you have a spouse or a partner who tends to get fired up and stressed out, and their negative energy causes your stomach to do flip flops, your heart to pound or brings up feelings of anger and bitterness. You can choose not to participate in their behavior. It doesn't mean you don't love them or care for them less; it is simply making a compromise and setting a boundary.

Recognize that often our boundaries are needed for our own behavior and thinking rather than for the words or actions of others. If commuting stresses you out, don't listen to the news or ruminate on thoughts that will make your mental health and time commuting worse. Use your commute time to let go of stress rather than inflame or hold on to it.

You can apply boundaries to any stressful situation. Do your best to remove yourself from the situation and step away from the drama. The hardest part of setting boundaries is actually sticking to them. No one can hold you accountable other than you.

Here is a formula you might find useful in applying this to your life. Apply the phrase below to a situation, and let it give you some direction in how to step out of stress. You will find that your biological response to socially stressful situations plays an essential part in compromising and setting boundaries. Thus, it is key to overcoming our biology.

"Situation W makes me miserable, frustrated, and hopeless [identify]. I feel this way because X [simplify]. I need to make a change, which means Y [compromise], and I will not let Z get in my way [boundary]."

Something to note while putting this into practice is that it can be easy to become disheartened while living the changes you envision. When you create and set boundaries to improve your health, happiness, and quality of life, not everyone will want to come along with you. Not everyone will embrace your changes or be ready to do the necessary work to better their lives. The idea here is that you must simply *start* and work with what you have, readdressing your situation as needed. The life you envision is attainable, but it will take time and effort. Take a leap and begin changing your life, doing what you can with what you have.

Remember, identify, simplify, compromise, and set boundaries. And then we move forward. If you want to change your life, all you have to do is change your life.

By working through stressful situations mindfully, we reprogram our brains. We train our brains to realize that although a situation may be stressful, it is not likely an immediate threat to our life. This is a necessary skill to cultivate because life doesn't slow down. Life always presents stressful situations. Thus it is up to you to identify stressful situations and understand the roots of the triggers. Decide what you will and will not compromise, set your boundaries and act to change the situation however you can.

What can you do to change your situation? Practice meditation, mindfulness, and proper breathing. Most of the time, the only thing you can change is yourself or how you respond. So adopting a meditation routine is one thing you can do to change your circumstances because it changes how you allow yourself to be affected by them. Many people roll their eyes at this idea because sometimes it is easier to avoid the situation than take the time to work through it. By utilizing meditation, mindfulness, and breathwork, we neither avoid the situation nor directly work through it. However, it is a calming step that allows us to detach from the drama a bit.

Once we've gained a bit of calm and distance, we work through the problem by identifying, simplifying, compromising, and setting boundaries. Meditation offers support when you're stressed, without taking action in any one direction. Meditation creates neutral disconnection so you can move forward productively and with support as you begin to create the life you want.

Once you adopt these techniques, over time and with practice, your nervous system will reprogram so that you can live your life with balance and clarity. However, to reap the benefits of meditation, you have to do the work.

It may feel tedious, but I know you can do it. Start small if you need to. Set your boundaries, follow through, and adjust accordingly. Whatever you do, *don't give up*. Adjust if you need to, but do not give up on your happiness.

The Take Away

The key point I want you to learn from this section is that our mind—in terms of biology, chemistry, and hormones—is structured to keep us alive, and a large part of staying alive is our fight-or-flight response. Our mind can be considered our emotional self. When we perceive a threat, will we fight or run? Although it served us well when survival was our primary goal in life, this automatic response has not adapted fast enough to keep up with our species' technological and social advancements. These days, our life can be lived more broadly than with a narrow focus on survival.

Our threats are now different and require a new response. Luckily, we have the mental capacity to realize this and adjust accordingly. This is where we overcome our biology and gain new techniques for facing our perceived threats. The first and most crucial step is understanding what these new threats are—which are different for everyone—and then overcoming our fear of these perceived threats.

Overcoming fear begins with the need to accept and feel pain. This can be said of emotional *and* physical pain, but we will focus on our aversion to emotional pain for now. Our fear of emotional pain manifests itself in insidious ways. Sometimes it becomes so deeply ingrained that we fear life itself—we become afraid to live.

Our response to fear triggers a chemical reaction that tells the body how to get back to a natural state of being— back into balance. This response amps up our nervous system, and over time can cause system dysfunction. Luckily you can train your brain to respond in healthier ways to everyday life by utilizing tools such as meditation, mindfulness, and breathing techniques. The more you practice these methods, the more efficiently your brain will identify what is and is not a threat.

My Experience and Beliefs

My ongoing battle with stress manifests itself in very tangible ways. As with most, stress affects my health. I'd go through periods where I was strong, healthy, and felt great. But I often cycled back to drastic weight loss, chronic pain, anxiety, depression, and a lack of desire to live. I eventually realized that stress was the culprit, but I had to go through alcohol addiction, panic attacks that landed me in the emergency room, and a vicious voice in my head telling me I would be better off dead. All this occurred while I was happily married, living in my dream home in the perfect little town.

If everything around me was so great, and I was living a perfect life, why was I miserable? Why was I taking on stress in a way that was literally going to kill me? Where were the stress and anxiety even coming from? Surely simply being alive isn't supposed to manifest anxiety, and I know I am not alive just to survive. Something had to give.

I hit my breaking point the night I drank so much I couldn't eat for the next two days without vomiting. I hit my breaking point when I saw myself in the mirror for the first time in months and realized that I already looked dead. Something. Had. To. Give.

It took reaching this point in my life to see that I needed to change what I was doing. I was not living the life I wanted for myself. In the chaos that I used to call living, I had lost sight that life is beautiful. I forgot that I had a purpose to serve. So what did I do? I started by identifying situations in my life that caused me unnecessary stress, and I learned how to stop the biological survival mechanisms that were leading me down a path of self-destruction.

I had spent years—more than a decade—living in a state of constant stress. This wired my brain so that my nervous system was constantly *on*. I was in a perpetual state of fight or flight. It began when I was nine and had no one to tell me what was happening to me or help me understand how to overcome my biology so that my mind and body could heal.

Your mind and body will heal only when in a state of rest and digest, so if you never allow your nervous system to disconnect and power down into rest mode, you are literally running your systems non-stop. You can only move through life this way for so long before you have system malfunctions. This is where my struggle with health began.

Every day, I live with Crohn's Disease, GERD, IBS, fibromyalgia, Raynaud's, hypermobility syndrome, thoracic outlet syndrome, autonomic dysfunction, scoliosis, sciatica, depression, and anxiety. This is not a cry for sympathy; it is simply the way it is—for now. Some of these health conditions arise from birth, but most of them developed over time because of my inability, or lack of knowledge, to overcome biology and step out of stress.

These conditions are not easy to live with, and after reaching the breaking points I mentioned earlier, I realized that the only way to feel good again was to get my health right. For me, this means hours of physical therapy and stress management—every day. It means a clean and pure diet free of processed foods and lots of water. I have learned to be extremely vigilant in how I treat my body.

As I realized what staying healthy meant for me, I also realized that I could not work a typical forty-hour-per-week job. At least not without jeopardizing my health and my life. I was at a crossroads, and this is where I began overcoming my biology and stepping out of stress. I began by *identifying the situation.*

For me, at first glance, it seemed that the stress culprit was my fluctuating health. However, once I simplified the situation, I realized my poor health was due to a lack of time given to healing. I was unable to commit enough time to healing because I was too busy dealing with commitments outside of myself. I was killing myself trying to live the "right" way—go to college, get a job, work forty to fifty hours a week, buy a house, and so on. I knew I needed to quit my job to take the necessary time to heal, but I was too afraid of being judged and other ramifications, so I kept trying to push on.

Eventually, I realized enough was enough. If I wanted a better life—a happy, healthy, beautiful life that I loved, I had to do what was necessary to get there. I decided to cut back my working hours so I could get my health and life back on track. I finally began moving in the right direction because I identified and simplified the situation, then made compromises and set boundaries.

My poor health caused unnecessary stress, so I had to compromise how much time I spent working. This compromise also meant that we would make less money while living in a house that we could barely afford. I knew I would compromise some comforts for the sake of my health and wellbeing, and we made it work for as long as we could keep compromising.

Time went on, and our situation continued to change. I could not return to work full time then the pandemic came. We needed to take more drastic measures; however, that is a story for another time. Ultimately, I want to make a very clear point about compromising—the most important factor about compromise is that although it is necessary, you must know your boundaries to make them benefit you. You also must be open to adjusting your boundaries as needed. In this situation, my boundary was not allowing other people's opinions of my life decisions to dictate how I felt about myself.

Through this experience, I learned it is not other people's opinion of you that matters; rather, it is your opinion of yourself that does. I had this notion that I had to be the best at everything and excel in everything that I did. And I used to. But when the time came for me to focus on healing, I kept pushing it off for fear that I wouldn't be good enough, or that I would let my family down, or that others would think of me as lazy.

All this changed after I set my boundaries. At first, I set them based on what I perceived was other people's opinions of me. However, I eventually realized I had to stop caring about what others thought of me. Their opinion could no longer dictate how I felt about myself. Over time I saw I needed to adjust my boundaries because I realized it was *my* self-doubt, and *my* expectations that had to be kept at arm's length, not what others thought of me or what *I thought* they thought.

After I identified and simplified the problem, decided what needed to be compromised, and set healthy boundaries around my thinking, my health and quality of life improved. Once I was no longer living a survival-based life, I had space to think about what kind of life I *really* wanted. Before this, my emotional self perceived social and economic situations as threatening. Therefore, I lived my life in a constant state of stress, with my nervous system working to the point of malfunction.

By deciding to change my life consciously, I overcame my brain and nervous system. I decided I would no longer live in self-doubt, fearing a perceived threat of not being good enough or not being liked. I would no longer allow my perception of others' opinions to dictate how I felt about myself or my decisions. I overcame my biology and stepped out of stress.

I will also add that I knew I needed help to crawl out of my hole. I stopped drinking, talked to my doctor, and started taking antidepressants. Two years later, I am pleased to say I no longer need the medication. Please get the help you need; so many avenues for help are available. You don't have to do it alone.

After these huge life-altering decisions and changes, I became pregnant with our lovely little boy. I continued to work on my health every day, continuously adjusting my boundaries and working through the remaining stressful situations. I quit my job, started a business, and we sold our house. It wasn't easy, and it took many compromises to get to where I needed to be to live a happy and healthy life, as well as boundaries that I absolutely had to stick to. Besides boundaries around my thoughts about myself and what others think, I also had to set tangible boundaries for my physical health. So without further ado, let's step into the next chapter, where we will explore the science behind physical health.

– Chapter 2 –

THE FOUNDATION OF HEALTH

The Main Lesson

This chapter will explore bodily physical health—separate from our mind and soul. We'll focus on the *physical self,* as well as biological aspects of how we function and how certain processes work together as a whole. The first aspect of physical health we will look at is hydration because it is fundamental to our body's wellbeing. Water is the foundation of life as we know it; water fills every inch of our being. Make water the center of your health. See where you can go when you hydrate properly.

Bodies are primarily made of water. It is not only the foundation of our physical body on a cellular level, but it also plays a crucial role in all the body's functions—everything from the fluid supporting our brain and spinal cord, the metabolization of carbs and proteins, to the transportation of oxygen throughout the body.

If our body is a vehicle, water is the oil; it keeps everything functioning and moving fluidly, including lubrication of joints and muscles, keeping skin supple, and helping the digestive system to move food and waste through our body. We require proper hydration levels for every part of our physical body, as well as for proper detoxification of the body. Thus, if we are not adequately hydrated, our body doesn't function as well. When our body doesn't function correctly over time, we have system failures.

Part of getting back to ground zero means living the way life intended you to live, mentally, physically, and spiritually. Living as we are intended, in a physical sense, means fueling our body properly. Here is a way to look at it you may not have heard before—you are not your body. Your body keeps you alive; therefore, you owe your life to your physical self. If you desire a happy, healthy life, you need to live as you were intended and take care of your physical self so it can take care of you.

Let's look at what happens when we neglect our bodies. First, we'll look at dehydration. I hope that learning these signs will help you identify when you are dehydrated. This is the first step in learning your requirements for hydration and building a solid foundation for your physical health.

Dehydration can be severe or chronic. Severe dehydration includes symptoms such as dark urine, fainting, rapid heartbeat, sunken eyes, and confusion, to name a few. Chronic dehydration occurs when you don't drink enough hydrating fluids over long periods. You might not notice the negative effects, or if you do, you don't attribute them to dehydration and therefore continue the cycle.

Chronic dehydration causes many health complications, and most of us aren't even aware we suffer from dehydration. Symptoms of chronic dehydration can include the severe symptoms listed above, as well as headaches, trouble focusing or concentrating, constipation, muscle weakness, fatigue, or cramping, compromised skin barrier, dry and flakey skin, dizziness, thirst, heart complications, the impaired ability for detox systems to function—such as kidneys, liver, and digestion —and the list goes on.

Perhaps you'll have a glass of water with a couple of meals throughout the week, but the rest of your fluids comes from sources other than water. Not to say that certain fluids can't hydrate you, but you have to be aware of what they are and if they are hydrating or not. The best method for ensuring you consume enough hydrating fluids daily is to stick to pure, unadulterated H_2O.

If you only have a couple of glasses or bottles of water throughout the week, it's safe to say you are not drinking enough. Or perhaps you might be the type to carry a water bottle around with you, filling it up occasionally but without intention throughout the day. This is better, but it may not be enough. Instead, aim for a certain goal every day. A great place to start is by drinking one-half of your body weight in liquid ounces. For example, if you weigh 180 pounds, try drinking 90 ounces of water every day or 60 ounces if you weigh 120 pounds. Start here and adjust as needed. If you are bothered that you have to use the restroom more, good. Your body's detox system is functioning well, and you should be grateful.

Everyone has different water requirements, and depending on age, weight, medications, or medical conditions, this can vary drastically. If you are on certain medications or have health conditions, you should always consult your doctor before trying anything new.

When not drinking enough water, you force your body to operate under physically stressful conditions. As we have learned, the key to living a happy, healthy life is to mitigate stress in as many ways as possible. In addition, depending on your diet and lifestyle, you might unintentionally increase these stressful conditions.

For example, some foods are extremely difficult to digest and filled with ingredients the body does not want nor need. Eating these foods causes the body to work harder while processing, detoxifying, and eliminating what we have consumed. The same goes for consuming coffee or alcohol. With the health of our body, hydration is two-fold—you must hydrate adequately for your needs, and you must know circumstances that increase dehydration.

I also want to bring forth the idea of becoming a steward of health. Part one of this book covers the fundamentals of maintaining the health of your emotional self and physical self, and it is only fitting that we discuss the mental shift which is required to achieve this. Building healthy habits, such as proper hydration, requires a certain level of dedication and commitment. You must shift your mindset to that of a steward of health.

Becoming a steward of health means you are an advocate for the health of what's inside you as well as what is outside of you. The environment which surrounds us dictates our immediate state of being. Just like how external stimulation causes a response in our brain via the nervous system, so too does our sight. It is one of our senses and thus responsible for taking in this stimulation. Our immediate external environment reflects what resides within us, whether it be harmony or chaos. When we take in the sights of our environment, this information goes into our mind, even when we try to pretend we don't see what's right in front of us.

If you want health, harmony, and happiness within you, you can start by creating it within your environment. As above so below, as within so without. It has been said that eyes are windows to the soul, after all.

The Take Away

The most important point of this section is that water is the foundation of all that we are. This compound founds all that creates us. It is life-giving and thus life-sustaining. In my opinion, water is the number one abused resource and is taken for granted by so many. It is a gift, just as our life is a gift.

Our bodies need this vital resource to function properly, and without enough of it, our physical bodies stop working correctly, our minds languish, and we are left shriveled and dried up—a walking corpse. So drink your water. Drink *clean water*. Drink the amount necessary for your body to function at its best—volumes vary by person. Drinking water is the most important habit you can build throughout this book, so do whatever is necessary to make it happen. Every. Single. Day.

This is the art of loving one's self and the first step in becoming a steward of health. Take care of what is inside of you, allow this self-care and love to be reflected out into your environment, and then back to you. As above so below, as within so without.

My Experience and Belief

Water is truly the gift of life. It is so profound that cultures and societies have created lore around it. It has been ascribed magical properties and has been used in sacred rituals for generations. We owe it reverence. We owe it respect. We should treat water like the life-giving gift that it is.

Water really is the foundation of life as we know it, and you can see the pattern of life within the journey water takes. It embodies a never-ending cycle of transformation, going from the oceans into the air, turning to rain, filling lakes and rivers, then going back out to the oceans again. Water doesn't resist transformation; it simply waits until circumstances are right and ever so effortlessly changes form. We should all strive to be more like water, allowing ourselves to flow and transform through the rocky shores of life, up into the clouds, and back down again. To be sturdy and slow-moving, yet strong enough and persistent enough to carve paths through mountains.

Where has all our water gone? It was never ours, to begin with, but we acted as though it was, and now the privilege is being removed. What will you do when it's all gone? These are questions we must ask ourselves now, and they are heavy.

I call upon the bottled water industry, our government, and individuals, saying do what you can, with what you have. Together we have the power to change the world for the better. We can save lives and save life itself. I'm not implying blame; instead, I want to open eyes to the condition of our physical, mental, and spiritual health and how it is being reflected back into the earth. I urge you to educate yourself on the condition of our planet. We are intrinsically connected to all that is around us, but we often forget and lose sight of what we are doing. Become the steward.

Stop letting other people decide what you think for you. Do your due diligence; if you need a sign to do better by our earth, this is it. What kind of world are we allowing when profit is gained from a limited, life-sustaining resource? Water is not a right; it is a gift—just like the plants, the sun, the moon, and your life. Treasure it, and do what you can with what you have.

We have completely forgotten the necessity of water. In our society—and by our, I am referring mainly to the United States, as this is my home—it has become ingrained for us to keep up with our neighbors or community. Keep going. Keep pushing. Go faster. Produce more. Consume more. More, more, more. It's losing its meaning. More to what end?

As my hairdresser Tina used to say in her East Coast accent, "Like come on, what are we doing here?" We are so caught up in "more" that we have forgotten what we actually need. Or want. We don't need more entertainment. We don't need more meat. We don't need more cell phones. We need more water—globally, nationally, locally, and individually. Our need for water is not only tangible, but it also needs to occupy mental space.

I urge you to *think* more about how much water you drink, as well as the source of water for your home. Where does it come from? What's in it? Water is a necessity for life and is imperative to your physical health.

– Chapter 3 –

Our Second Brain and Its Ecosystem

The Main Lesson

In the first chapter, we discussed how emotions and signals to the brain affect our nervous system. Now we have another system that needs to be addressed, the digestive system. It's a broad topic, and this book's scope will talk about the digestive system from two perspectives —the outer world and nervous system, and our inner world and gut flora.

The digestive system is our second brain. Have you ever heard the saying, "Trust your gut?" Why do you feel butterflies in your stomach when you are excited or feel nauseous when you are nervous? What is it about these emotions which affect our bodily systems? These feelings arise largely from our enteric nervous system, and it consists of nerves and neurons which line our digestive tract.

In addition to these nerves are billions of microscopic organisms, which create our gut flora and is how our food gets digested. These microbes also play a large role in sending correct hormones and chemicals to our brains.

Our digestive system is like a microscopic ecosystem, with its very own brain. I want to go back to what I mentioned in the last chapter, looking at physical health as our body being completely separate from our mind and soul. That's because it is separate. This is our *physical self.*

This is where my next point for a happy and healthy life comes in—the mind-body connection. Some refer to this as the mind-gut connection. Let's break it down again; our nervous system responds to chemical signals we send to it, which are emotional responses to stimulation. We can say this in terms of our five senses: sight, sound, smell, taste, and feel. But can't it also be said of the elusive sixth sense, your gut feeling? Also known as your *intuition.* What signals are our gut sending to our brain? Most research surrounds the idea that the central and peripheral nervous systems affect the digestive system, but not as much is said about how our digestive system affects the rest of us.

We often overlook the digestive system when considering the health of our mind and body, but the connection between the two is essential. The digestive system spans almost the entire central nervous system. Not only that, but our digestive system breaks down food and turns it into useful resources. These resources get used by our bodily functions, are turned into new cells, and then what is left is excreted. This is detoxifying the body.

Our digestive system is not only close in proximity to the central nervous system but also responds to our fight-or-flight reactions. If we are in fight or flight, typically, our mind tells our body to turn off our digestive system. You don't want to poop in the woods if you are face-to-face with a bear. These days, although we are generally out of the woods, we often still behave in a manner that tells our minds that we are in danger.

To tie in examples from the first chapter, if we do not have a supportive mind-body connection, our nervous system will respond incorrectly to external inputs. In other words, we'll act like we're face-to-face with a bear in the woods when in reality, we're in a traffic jam. This automatic yet confused behavior of our body is affected by two things—external inputs and how our mind makes sense of them, and our internal gut biome. Both mind and body need to be balanced before you step out of stress and begin living the life you desire.

I know this is a lot to take in, so before moving on, I want to reiterate that our digestive system is our second brain and hosts a strong connection between our mind and body. Therefore, what we eat and how it gets digested has a tremendous impact on our body's hormonal and chemical makeup. If we do not have a healthy gut biome, our digestive system cannot effectively use the food we eat.

I am not a doctor, nor am I a nutritionist; however, I have never heard nor been told that a non-processed, balanced diet would be detrimental to someone's health. In fact, it is very much the opposite. You literally are what you eat, and although this is a drastically simplified statement, your cells are made up of what you consume. Additionally, if you don't give your body the necessary tools to break down your food, how can the food be digested? If you are not giving your body the nutrition to support a strong, functional body, how can it be strong or functional?

The mind-body connection is extremely complex, as is our relationship with the microorganisms within us. Nutrition is an integral part of how your mind and body feel, as well as how your mind and body act. The awareness of this connection is important, as is the awareness of how you are or are not supporting it. Now that we have explored the digestive system and its relationships to the body, it is up to you to further learn about your second brain and internal microscopic ecosystem.

The Take Away

The digestive system is extremely complex, but we have explored two essential aspects of this system and how it affects our wellbeing. The first aspect to consider is our bacteria-rich gut biome. We aren't born with a microbiome; we have a blank slate at birth, and it takes maintenance via proper diet to cultivate a healthy one.

The second aspect to consider is the digestive system as a whole. It does not merely digest food, but serves as a second brain, separate from our mind. We know this system as our enteric nervous system that works in tandem with the central and peripheral nervous systems. I like to think of our gut biome as the central brain, with the digestive tract being the nervous system.

Without healthy or good bacteria in the right places, the appropriate amount of bacteria, and effective food to feed these microbes, our biome-brain dies, leaving it susceptible to harmful bacteria, illness, and disease. Our enteric nervous system and internal ecosystem are the driving forces of our physical body and constitute a large portion of our chemical and hormonal makeup.

All we ingest gets disassembled and turned into building blocks for our bodies; you are what you eat, but it's not really *you* who's eating. Be a steward and be nice to your microbes. Just like water, they are part of what's keeping you alive.

My Experience and My Belief

I received a Crohn's disease diagnosis in September 2015. The stress of my mother's illness and the unexpected passing of a dear friend shook me to my core. I could not stand up straight nor move for about three days. At that point, I decided it was time to talk with a professional. I ended up in the ER, and although the doctor couldn't diagnose me, he told me my CT showed there was something wrong with my large intestine. They discharged me with instructions to schedule a colonoscopy—I have now had six of these procedures, and those are enough motivation to do whatever I could to get myself into remission.

The results came back as expected, and I officially received the diagnosis of Crohn's disease. Crohn's is hereditary, and my mother had a very severe case. We expected that I, too, had the disease, but it was not previously detectable. My mother's condition was so extreme that it disabled her, and I believe it contributed to her inability to survive cancer—that's a story for another time. Crohn's disease affects the entire digestive tract, all the way from one end to the other, and causes ulcers, bowel obstruction, severe inflammation, fistulas, fissures, and more. It can also affect the body's ability to absorb nutrients.

For example, my mother was about 5' 4" and rarely weighed over 100 pounds. Because of the severity of her condition, she had feet of digestive tract removed but was lucky enough to avoid a colostomy bag—a common reality for people with Crohn's disease. This disease can debilitate and potentially threaten your life. Current knowledge indicates that it is a hereditary immune disorder brought on by environmental factors. That's it. That's all the scientific community knows about this disease.

Maybe I'm not giving the science and medical communities enough credit. Advances in knowledge and treatment have evolved, but research is slow going. Treatments, which may lead to remission, include suppressing our immune system—the system which also detects and fights cancer. My mother found great relief from one of the newer biological drugs that suppress the immune system. She was finally pain-free and could enjoy food again for the first time in about thirty years. She said she felt so good that she could go back to work again, but there was a catch. If my mom went back to work, she would lose her free health insurance, and therefore could not afford the treatment.

I watched her suffer from this disease from the time I was three years old until she died, two months after my diagnosis. My mom once told me that had she known that she had Crohn's disease, she wouldn't have had me for fear that I too would develop the disease. My relationship with Crohn's, and the digestive system, is deep.

My diagnosis came when I was in my junior year of college, and after taking time off to settle my mother's estate, I went back to finish my bachelor's degree. During this time, I began receiving treatment for Crohn's. I tried two different biologic drugs, but I found that the side effects weren't worth it for me at that point in time. It took years of learning to listen to my body before understanding what it was trying to tell me.

I found that the harder I worked myself to participate in life, the worse my condition became. However, it wasn't necessarily this participation that caused the deterioration, but rather a decrease in my tolerance to stress which occurred while participating. Let me tell you, as someone with generalized anxiety—and just having lost my mother —my stress tolerance at that point was nonexistent. Participating in life became nothing more than living to survive.

After almost an entire lifetime of suppressed stress and trauma, I couldn't take on any more. Many emotions that I had pushed down and ignored began to manifest as deteriorating mental and physical health. However, it took a long time to realize trauma suppression caused the acceleration of Crohn's and the decline of my mental health. Much like our central and peripheral nervous systems, our enteric nervous system has its own response to stress and an ability for fight or flight.

I needed to strengthen the connection between both nervous systems so that my mind and gut were in sync and I could better understand the truth behind what stimulation I was taking in. Through my healing process, I learned I am easily overstimulated. This understanding brought forth healing. Over time, I have become much better at tolerating stress and stimulation; I know when to say I've had enough.

This self-understanding did not come easily. It took years of trial and error and learning before I could piece together how disjointed my nervous systems were, as well as the effect it was having on my mind and body. It took slowing down and listening to what my body was trying to tell me.

I used the lessons I discussed in previous sections to overcome my biology and social conditioning to hear the cries of my mind and body. It takes time and practice, but I know you can do it too. Remember: identify the situation, understand what's really causing your response, compromise, and set boundaries. Wash, rinse, repeat.

I'd like to leave you with one last vital piece of information. To have a healthy enteric nervous system, the ecosystem which supports it must be healthy as well. Therefore, what you consume plays a vital role in the health of your mind and body. It's not about calories, or fat, or the number on the scale. An unstable foundation has an insidious effect on your health; it's safe to assume that you don't know the full extent or depth of how your consumption affects you. Take the time necessary to learn so that you can heal what you might not even know needs healing.

– Chapter 4 –

MOVEMENT AND CONNECTING TO OUR PHYSICAL SELF

The Main Lesson

So far, we have discussed mind and body health in terms of our nervous and digestive systems. We have taken the approach of viewing these aspects as emotional and physical versions of ourselves. This next section brings forth the importance of using movement to improve the health of our circulatory and immune systems, which are vital pieces to this physical version of us. You have to start with the health of each piece in order to achieve health within the whole system.

My goal for this section is to help you understand the importance of movement for the health of your body and the health of our species. We'll start with an overview of the systems I mentioned, and then I'll move on to an explanation of how our species has changed over time in terms of movement and decision-making. You might not expect it, but these two ideas go hand-in-hand.

The circulatory system cycles blood and oxygen throughout our bodies. We have two types of circulation, pulmonary and systemic. Pulmonary circulation cycles blood between the heart and lungs to oxygenate the blood, and systemic circulation cycles oxygenated blood throughout the rest of our body. Having enough oxygenated blood coursing throughout your body is essential for brain and motor function, as well as for proper nerve function.

If you have poor circulation, you often have cold and or tingling extremities, can have a purple-blue and pale complexion, or if you aren't receiving enough oxygen to your brain, you can feel lightheaded, faint, or confused. Although these symptoms can stem from various issues, they can also be indicators that your body's circulation system is not working as well as it needs to.

Physically moving your body, even at a slow pace, can help with circulation by literally moving blood cells throughout your body. Increasing your cardiovascular activity helps improve circulation exponentially because you are forcing your lungs and heart to work harder—moving oxygenated blood at a faster pace than while you are at rest. Over time, your heart and lungs become more accustomed to this increase in oxygen and faster recycling rate, and much like our muscles, they get stronger, and toxins move out of our body faster. Many systems in our body work this way, including our immune system.

The immune system is another highly complex system in terms of how it works, how it is affected, and how it affects our body. Because of its complexity, the explanation here is going to be short and to the point. In sum, the immune system is our body's defense against microscopic organisms and toxins which can make us sick. These organisms are usually viruses, bacteria, fungi, parasites, toxic chemicals, and so on.

Next, we'll explore our lymphatic system and discuss its role in protecting our bodies from the above-listed organisms and toxins, as well as its job of removing waste and abnormal cells from the body. The lymphatic system is part of our immune system.

The lymphatic system is much like internal webbing, similar to nerve and blood pathways, which span your entire body. This system includes pathways, nodes, and organs that work together to filter lymph, a fluid produced by your body filled with white blood cells. Although it has multiple functions, the primary job of our lymphatic system is to get lymph out of our tissue and muscles and into our bloodstream, where it can be recycled.

Our cells and tissues drain lymph, and in addition to excess fluid and white blood cells, lymph also contains potentially harmful substances. As lymph cycles through your body, it comes to points within your system called lymph nodes. These nodes filter the lymph to remove any harmful substances. Our lymphatic system also helps maintain normal fluid levels in the body, as it takes excess fluid from our cells and tissues, filters it, and then puts it back into our bloodstream.

Failure of the lymphatic system, and its symptoms, are beyond the scope of this book. However, I will say that this system is integral to our immune and circulatory system, so we must treat it nicely for it to function effectively. The best way to be kind to your lymphatic system is to refrain from overindulging in harmful substances. Just like any system, if it becomes overtaxed, it will not work as well as necessary to keep our body balanced and healthy. Remember, become a steward.

Another key factor to the health of our lymphatic system, and therefore our immune system, is movement! Yes, here we are, back to basics. Just as movement helps circulate blood and oxygen, it also helps to circulate lymphatic fluid. In this case, movement is a necessity, as our lymphatic system doesn't have the benefit of a pump like our circulatory system does. Our lymphatic system requires physical movement—via exercise, massage, or dry-brushing—to work correctly.

Now that you have a basic understanding of how a couple of critical body systems function and why they need movement to work at their best, we'll switch gears and explore our movement habits as a species. Let's go over how they have changed, how this change has negatively affected us, and how changing your movement habits will help you in living the life you want.

To start, let's look at an overview of how and why our movement habits have changed. Humans used to spend days being very active. But now, thanks to technology and lifestyle, we have become a rather sedentary species. We, mostly, no longer have to run to catch our food and no longer live with survival as our primary drive. This is all splendid news; however, this change of life has also negatively affected our long-term health.

Yes, we are no longer face-to-face with danger and survival daily, and this means we don't have to push our bodies to extreme physical limits and be as physically strong as we once were. But by becoming more sedentary and forgetting our basic biological needs, our health is now threatened by obesity, heart disease, and other life-ending illnesses. This new life-way has existed long enough that our children are born with the genetics that predisposes them to these illnesses.

Our species is still threatened, but the threat has changed from short-term to long-term, and unfortunately, our decision-making capabilities are having a hard time catching up. Recall the story from Chapter One, where we discussed our outdated nervous system. When our threats were short-term, our short-term decision-making served us well. Now that our threats have changed, we need our decision-making to change along with them. Let's look at this idea a little closer.

Besides living to survive, we also made very short-term decisions based on our immediate threats and dangers. We based our decisions on fear and the avoidance of pain; it was necessary for survival. Now, we no longer need to live this way, yet we still allow our short-term decision-making —based on fear and the avoidance of pain—to lead our lives.

For example, many people who live sedentary lives know lack of movement is bad for them. Even those who are relatively active often recognize that they need to move more to maintain or improve their health and longevity. However, to make that lifestyle change, a person has to go through discomfort and some pain. So usually, the change never happens because they will make a short-term decision based on fear and the avoidance of pain. This is shortsighted.

To make a long-term decision, they have to overcome their fear of pain and discomfort, knowing that it will lead to a longer and healthier life. It is something to note, too, that this discomfort can be physical or be based around needing to *change*. Change often makes people uncomfortable.

Much like our biological responses to fear and threats, our decision-making also hasn't adapted with lifestyle and technology changes. We have allowed the automation of our lives to overcome our abilities as human beings. Our bodies were capable of such amazing things, and we took this for granted; now, we are losing our ability to think clearly, breathe, and move. Our systems are failing us.

We are not just dying; we're slowly losing our ability to live. Our children are now born with genes that may predispose them to a life of pain and suffering. Luckily, we can readjust so that the future of our species remains intact. If you have food, water, and shelter, and you are not face-to-face with a metaphorical bear, you have your life. If you want to improve your life, you need to reprogram your decision-making.

To wrap up this section, I'll bring back the example of the short-term decision to avoid movement because it is uncomfortable, even though we know a long-term sedentary lifestyle can lead to life-threatening illnesses. When examining this thought process in relation to building movement habits, we see the hardest part is starting. Getting out of your comfort zone of being sedentary is going to be uncomfortable and a little painful. There is no way around that.

If you want to improve your movement habits, move. Move past the discomfort and pain. I promise, the more you do it, the easier it gets. This is where reprogramming your decision-making comes in; you must learn the difference between pain that will kill you and pain that is good for you. If you base decisions around pain avoidance, you will never do the things which cause you pain, even if they are good for you. Get over it. Sorry, it's the truth, and gentler words won't change that.

To improve your life, health, and decision-making, you will have to do things you don't want to do. The longevity of our species, and the health of our children, are at stake here. So, let's upgrade our biological selves into a version of us that will carry our species into the future.

That said, if you have specific illness or health restrictions, please talk to your doctor before starting anything new. Whether you plan to run marathons, hike mountains, or walk around the block, it is crucial to know your health's boundaries and limitations. Your body is capable of amazing things. You are strong. You are adaptive. You are a creature made to move. Honor this by allowing space in your life for movement.

Choose to practice intentional movement and move your body in ways that may stretch your comfort zone, just ever so slightly. We cannot know what we are capable of until we reach the outer limits of these capabilities. But you mustn't rush. Or strain. Or try to push yourself past this point—at least before you are ready to. In this balance, we find peace within the movement and peace within ourselves; and each individual's point of balance is ever-changing as they move along in their journey.

The Take Away

Breaking down the science behind moving our physical bodies and its effect on our wellbeing can either be straightforward, or we can become entangled (physics joke) by thinking about the relationship between our micro-macro selves. I will not dive into micro-macro duality or Newton's Law of Motion, so let us just say, when we move our body externally, similar movements occur on a cellular level. Hang upside down, and blood rushes to your head. Swing your arms, and blood flows to your hands and fingers.

The take away from this section is that we need to move our body to move what's inside our body, such as our blood and lymphatic fluid. Red blood cells contain oxygen and are cycled through our body via our circulatory systems, while white blood cells, which fight infections, are cycled through our lymphatic system. Physical movement moves oxygen and immune fighting cells throughout our body, making it another vital aspect of our physical wellbeing.

However, technological advancements have led to a large part of our species becoming sedentary. For some of us, movement has become too far out of the norm, and we often believe it takes too much effort. Our decision-making around the avoidance of pain and fear is a biological survival mechanism; therefore, we choose to avoid movement because it seems painful. So here we are again, needing to overcome our biology. This time, though, we will step into movement.

My Experience and Belief

Before moving on to Part Two, where we begin our journey inward, I want to take a minute to share my experience with overcoming fear-based decision making around physical movement, as this is something I have had to do many, many times from living with chronic pain.

Most of my disorders and illnesses come from stress management, but a few are from being hyper-mobile. Because of the brain's response to pain and discomfort, it often causes a feedback loop of terrible and excruciating symptoms.

For example, I have tendon and nerve impingements in both shoulders, scoliosis, sciatica, subluxing joints, a neck injury, and TMJ. All of these conditions are painful, but to top it off, I developed fibromyalgia, an autonomic nervous system dysfunction, and Raynaud's syndrome. Pain from musculoskeletal instability—in other words, being hypermobile—causes fibromyalgia and other issues to worsen. This leads to increased pain, the long-term stress of which triggers a Crohn's flare-up and fibromyalgia to worsen. The constant pain beat up my nervous system, and at some point, I had to teach my brain and my body that this pain would not kill me, even if it felt like it was. I had to overcome my biology and rewire my brain to respond to all types of stimulation appropriately.

I eventually realized this was just part of the life I was destined to live, and I had to get over the discomfort—and my fear of it—because it would not go away. I will live with this physical pain, or the potential of it, every day for the rest of my life. To have any shred of normalcy or relief, I can't afford to allow myself to fear the pain or have any amount of self-pity because doing so makes the situation worse. Instead, I allow the pain to run its course and let it pass through. But to do this, I have to come face-to-face with it, stare it in the eyes, and allow it to be. I've taught my mind that this pain will not kill me, and in turn, I have created the ability within myself to let the pain teach me. Learning to listen to the tells of your body is a life skill imperative to living a happy and healthy life.

Through this long grappling fight with pain, I have learned that it is how our body tells us when something might not be right. But I have also learned that sometimes things that don't feel good need to happen—for example, working my muscles and moving my body despite the pain or exhaustion. There's no point in avoiding it because you are just trading short-term pain and discomfort for long-term pain.

When you are ready to improve your physical health through movement, you must jump in. Do it even though you're scared—of pain, discomfort, judgment, of feeling like a failure, or feeling like you're not good enough. Instead of turning away in fear, breathe into it, and let it be until that emotion has run its course. You will be stronger for it.

Breathing, meditating, eating well, and moving my body are all therapies and coping mechanisms I have developed for managing pain and mental health, and I mostly have these conditions managed very well. That's not to say every day is perfect, but changing my decision-making from short-term to long-term helped create habits that allow me to live a relatively pain-free and healthy life—physically and emotionally. As a result, I am no longer debilitated by my pain and can look forward to a future that I want to be a part of. I am living the life I truly want.

Overcoming our biology is about facing our fears and reprogramming our thinking—changing all mental and physical aspects to be in line with this new version of ourselves, who is not afraid to reach for the life we want. You are creating who you want to be. But to create this version of yourself, you have to make peace with all the experiences that brought you to this point. Holding on to the past prevents you from freely moving forward into the future version of yourself. A happier and healthier you, ready to create a life with meaning.

The first part of this book emphasizes our biological health in terms of mind and body. We started here because physical health is the foundation from which to grow. When your base needs aren't met—the conditions that support the wellbeing of the mind and body—you can't expect yourself to move beyond your current circumstances. Instead, you will backslide and always feel as though something is missing.

The proper function of biological mechanisms creates our wellbeing; our mind-body is a machine. You need each part to function at its best for the whole to be at peak performance. Therefore, you cannot have wellbeing—or be well—if either the mind or the body is not well.

It is essential to understand your bodies' systems and requirements before building healthy habits that contribute to living the life you want. This means getting control over your nervous systems, changing your decision-making, and giving your body the resources it needs to be well.

By the end of this book, you will have tools to help you feel in control of your reality so that you can passionately step into a life that has meaning. But getting to that point takes more than healthy habits alone; you also need to know what kind of life you want to live.

– Part Two –

Becoming Our Original Self

To move forward, you must let go of what's holding you back. In the previous section, I discussed letting go of fear, stepping out of stress, and becoming a steward of health to help us gain clarity and strength in our life. Next, we will clear out any negative or stuck energy and call back our original self so that our life can align with who we are on a soul level.

However, before we get to a point where we can clear out old energy, we need a solid belief of *what* this energy is and how it moves throughout us. The next chapter will explain a concept which I call the *energetic self*, as well as how to harness this energy through meditation and mindfulness.

You can live any life you want, but one undeniable and unbreakable law of life is that intention means nothing without action. How we act determines the life we live. If you want to live a life that serves your soul's purpose, live according to your soul—in a way that resonates with your authentic self.

It's time to decide what you believe. You must feel, even if it's just a little, that you have a purpose. Just like you must believe you have a soul, you believe that you have a life calling and that you came to the earth for a reason. Odds are you wouldn't be reading this book if you didn't, or if you at least want to believe it. So, even if you are on the fence, humor me.

The discussion ahead can only help you if you surrender your current opinions and leave life up to multiple interpretations. For some people, it is easier to deny the idea that they have a purpose and life calling than to accept their role. Once they believe in themselves, they have to change, and not all will do the work.

One thing to consider is that you are not a martyr. You don't have it worse than anyone else. Stop sulking and feeling sorry for yourself. You are not weak, nor are you helpless. No one is going to do this for you. If you want to live a better life, it is time to step up and do what needs to be done. If you want to follow your life's calling, find your soul's purpose, and live the life you want, you must love yourself—love your mind, love your body, love your soul —the authentic you. Love yourself so hard that you learn to believe in your capabilities and know your worth. You are worth health and happiness; you are worth a soulful life.

I know it's hard to believe in something that seems to have no tangible evidence. This is what we call faith. You have the choice to live life with faith or to live life without. The choice is yours alone to make, but you must decide. Choosing faith means surrendering to the unknown yet knowing you can achieve anything you set your mind to.

Choosing faith in yourself is how you unlock the door to your soul's purpose. It's what leads you to the life you want. To know what you want, you must know yourself. To know yourself, you must know where you've been. This is the never-ending cycle of humanity.

Let's get started on learning about our energetic self, remembering where we've been, and exploring who we are and what we want. Uncover your soul's purpose and retrieve your original self from layers of life experience.

– Chapter 5 –

FINDING YOUR LIFEFORCE

As we move through this book, we begin with creating health by building habits around how we treat our emotional and physical selves. Now we have moved into a transition phase between the biological and spiritual— between science and soul. This is the energetic self.

The concept of having an energetic self has been accepted across the world in many different cultures and spiritual practices. Western society today is much more accepting of this concept than it was, say, 60 or 70 years ago. If you are unsure, I ask again that you humor me on this still theoretical concept. At least for the sake of this book.

Energy is our life force and has had names such as qi, prana, and ka, to name a few. It flows through our bodies along specific pathways and pools into designated areas, mostly along our spinal cord. As this life force pulses through us, we emit an energetic field; this is our aura, also called our light body. We now have the ability to take a picture of our aura by recording our electromagnetic field and turning it into corresponding colors, thus proving its existence.

I use three different classification systems to describe the energetic body and life force from which it is created. These classifications have come from ancient societies in China, India, Egypt, and multiple geographic locations where shamanism has thrived.

Throughout history, we, as humans, have known of this invisible force that drives our desire for life. What is the meaning of life? What is the soul? What does it mean to ascend?

We've aspired to answer these questions since the dawn of our existence. Or, as some people believe, since we forgot our origins and purpose.

Try as we might, the concept of energy is something that cannot be fully explained or understood. It is something that we feel within us. This is different from feeling physically or emotionally; we feel it *spiritually*.

For the purpose of this chapter, I will mostly refer to *chakra* theory. This is the foundation of the meditation and breathwork I mention in Chapter One.

In order to create a life true to our soul, we must be aligned to do so within every facet of us. This means mentally and emotionally, physically, and the actions we take.

To bring these different aspects into alignment, we can use meditation and breathwork. This calms our nervous system and allows for clear thinking. Thus, our actions become clear, precise, and grounded in what is true to us.

We will start with a breathing technique called *belly breathing*.

The concept is relatively simple. Breathe in and out of your nose, image each inhalation reaching all the way to your belly, expanding it. As you exhale, your belly contracts.

When you are ready, fill your belly with air, allow your diaphragm to expand, and then fill your lungs last. Take as big of a breath as you can manage without your shoulders moving.

Hold.

Then, exhale, starting with the air in your belly, ending with the air in your lungs. Try to exhale completely, like life is giving you a hug so tight it squeezes all the air out of you. This is the most important step.

As you exhale, it may be helpful to make a sound; the sound allows you to lean into your exhale and can be useful if you are particularly tense or just starting out. Think of it as a big sigh of relief.

Hold. Inhale again, filling your belly first. Repeat.

Breath is life. As we breathe in, we fill our bodies with compounds necessary for survival. Now, I want you to imagine breathing in energy. This energy is a pure life force granted to us by the Divine.

Allow yourself to fall into an easy pattern of breathing from your belly, with the thought of filling yourself with this pure Divine energy. Imagine your body absorbing it not only through your lungs but through your skin.

As you absorb and breathe in this energy, it fills you. As you exhale, you let go of what no longer serves your highest purpose. Exhale hate, anger, greed, lust. What comes to mind will vary from person to person, and only you can know what you need to release.

Now we will add a *chakra meditation* to this breathing technique.

Continue breathing deeply and steadily, then move your focus to the base of your spine. This is the area where your legs connect with your body, the base of your physical self —your root. This is what grounds you to reality and the earth around you.

The base of your spine is where your root chakra is located. It is associated with feelings of security and the color red.

Breathe in pure white light energy. When you inhale, direct this energy to the spot at the base of your spine. When exhaling, imagine breathing out the color red.

While working on this chakra, remind yourself that you are safe. You are secure. You are supported. You are.

We will continue up our spine, ending at the top of our head, focusing on one chakra at a time. Each time you breathe in, you moving energy and intention into that point. You may find that some points are harder for you than others. You may become emotional or feel pain in certain areas of your body. This is okay; there's no need to fight these feelings. Acknowledge, accept, and allow it to be what it is.

Move your focus upwards to just below your navel. This is your sacral chakra and corresponds with creativity and passion. Envision the color orange. Continue your breathing, exhaling orange, reminding yourself that you were born to create. You are creative and have great passion. You feel.

Find the center of yourself inside the bottom of your ribcage, your solar plexus. This chakra is the color yellow. You are confident, joyful, and capable. You can.

Move up to your sternum, between your breasts, and by your heart. Breathe out green, remembering that you come from unconditional love and love unconditionally. You love and are loved.

Above your heart chakra, you have your throat chakra. Fill yourself with pure energy and exhale blue. You speak your truth clearly. You communicate and express yourself freely. You speak.

Move up to a spot in the center of your forehead, between your eyes. Find your third eye and exhale indigo. This is the center of your intuition. You are intuitive; your intuition guides you, and you know your truth. You see.

Now you have arrived at the crown of your head. This point is violet and connects you to the Divine. You are connected to the Divine. You are one with Creation. You have an open mind. You understand.

This concludes our breathing and visualization practice. Practice this technique as often as you can. Personally, I do this every day. Taking at least 10-20 minutes out of your day to sit in stillness and contemplation is crucial to your mental, physical, and spiritual health.

Now that we have an understanding of what energy is and how it affects us, we can move into the next portion of this book, where we clear out old, stagnant, and negative energy in order to uncover and heal our original self.

This uncovering will shine a light on certain memories, and memories hold emotions. Emotions hold energy. We want to keep our energy balanced and constantly flowing through us; therefore, we want to let our emotions flow as well. To do this, we will meet our inner child and take a close look at the memories which hold emotion for us.

– Chapter 6 –

MEETING OUR ORIGINAL SELF AND OBSERVING OUR PAST

We have come to the exploration of the soul. In this chapter, we will use visualization activities to meet and understand our inner child. Our inner child is the original version of ourselves, before the trauma and heartache that life brings. It is our authentic self, the most innocent and wholehearted part of us.

In this exploration, we will face our fear of the past, learn that it is okay to feel joy and pain, and understand that it's okay to be gentle. Just as we make decisions and take actions to avoid pain and fear, we avoid working through our past because doing so forces us to face the emotional pain we experienced as a child. Do not minimize or hide from your past experiences; they have made you who you are. Instead, you can choose to release the emotions and move into the version of yourself you want to be.

Much of our emotional healing comes from going back in time, so we can understand how and why certain events influenced us. This understanding helps us learn how we changed from them. To create the life you want, you must know what you want and know where you have been.

We will go through a series of visualizations so that you can meet this original version of yourself and take an objective backseat view of your life story. The hope is that after you meet your original self, you can move forward to identify how your life story shaped your beliefs and built your value systems. Once you observe your values objectively, you can question your perceptions and decide what you'd like to let go of to make room for that which speaks to the life you want to live.

We often think without thinking, thus perpetuating a life that does not resonate with us as it maybe once did. This next section is not to be taken lightly, and it will not be easy. I invite you to rise to the occasion and take the necessary steps to break down everything that you think you know so that you can rebuild and create a life that you love and identify with.

However, revisiting old wounds can be dangerous. If you feel like something is too hard to work through in this setting, it is a sign that you should seek help from a professional who can work with you in person. I am not a licensed therapist, and this book is not to meant to replace professional help. It is okay to ask for help, especially with such sensitive topics. The bottom line is, if you want to make room in your life for more of what you want, you need to work through your perceived problems so that you can move past them. You create your life whether you are aware of it or not.

Put intentional and mindful effort into each visualization. Read through each section, one piece at a time, then close your eyes and give the exercise your best effort. The fewer distractions you have, the better, and remember that you will begin as an objective observer through these exercises. You are separate from the child you envision. Envision yourself as a stranger observing the life story of this child.

Exercise One
The Practice

So, for our first exercise, I invite you to go back to your child self and think about who you were. Contemplate the very first version of yourself that you can remember. Envision this child as if you are an observer.

What is she wearing? Is she inside? Outside? What is surrounding her? How does she interact, play, smile, cry? What are her fears and fascinations? Now, hold on to the image of this child that you have conjured up. Keep her there in the front and center of your mind. What is her passion? When is she the most joyful?

See if you can feel her innocence and natural desire to love. I want you to feel the innocence and love of this child deeply. If you don't think it's there, you haven't gone far enough back. If you need to, go back to before you think you can remember. What is one of the first things you felt, heard, tasted, or smelled? Feel the innocence you had before the world around you shaped your perceptions of what was real and what wasn't before you knew what was safe and what wasn't.

It is okay to feel this and to hold on to it. This doesn't make you weak or naïve. It makes you human, as this is how you came to the world. Contemplate your description of this child and the thoughts and feelings evoked.

The Lesson

The lesson of this practice is to remember who you were when you came into the world. Doing this with the detachment of an observer takes away any of the conditioned thoughts you have about yourself. To get back to your original self, you have to know who that person was, as this is who you are under the layers of conditioning brought on by other people.

I believe you come into the world as who you are meant to be. And you will find no satisfaction in being anything other than that. Over time we lose track of this original version of ourselves. Through this process of visualization, we will remember ourselves one piece at a time.

Once you have started the exercise, you will find memories come back to you over days, weeks, or even months. As you begin remembering this child, your original self will take shape. This is not an exercise you will do once, but many times as memory pieces come back to you.

My Experience and Belief

When looking back at my child self, I see a little girl with bare feet and dirt on her face. Mountains, tall grass, flowers, mossy rocks, frogs, and salamanders surround her, and she has a camera in her hand.

As I hold this vision, my childhood passions come back to me bit by bit—baking, building, reading, drawing, star gazing, foraging. My heart always came back to one essential thing—creating. Whether with words, pictures, sounds, by hand, or by thought, my heart wanted to bring forth a unique beauty for the delight of others. It was a beauty that you feel. I wanted to evoke emotion and bring feeling back into the world.

I soon found my niche in words and storytelling. I remember that before I could even read or write, I would tell stories and have my family draw pictures to illustrate them for me. I had one particular caretaker who played a special role in building my passion for creativity. His name was George; I loved him as a grandfather and best friend. He lived with us and watched me while my parents were working or with friends. Just as my mother gave me a passion for the earth, George gave me a passion for creativity.

It was sometime between the first and third grades when I gave up the art of storytelling for the first time. We were learning sentence structure in school, and my teacher said I was using commas incorrectly.

My innocent voice asked, "But I thought you said we use them when we want a pause in our sentence?"

"Well, yes, but not like that," she replied.

Ouch. I was shunted into a remedial writing and reading class because they thought I just "didn't get it." This was a point of pain for me and destroyed my self-esteem and creativity. From that point on, I was no longer interested in school, learning, or creating.

My mom pulled me out of public school in the third grade and homeschooled me while we lived in Mexico during my father's cancer treatment. I did so well that when we got back three months later, I was way ahead of the rest of the class. It excited me to learn again, and my confidence returned. So when we got our first computer a couple of years later, I spent my time writing books. I was eleven years old.

When I got to high school, I kept my writing a quiet secret, scribbling poems and cascading thoughts in my diary as I tried to get a grip on anything, anything at all, that might bring me up to the surface of the emotional ocean I was drowning in. By this point, the turmoil from losing my father and having a volatile home life had taken a heavy toll. I was also still hurting and holding on to the idea that I wasn't any good, so I never shared my passion for fear that I would be told again I wasn't skilled enough.

I pushed my passion for creativity farther and farther away, keeping it hidden from others for so long that it became hidden even from myself. It wasn't until I was halfway through college—right before my mom got sick —that I began to shine light into those dark, dusty corners of my mind. I had forgotten about the little girl who loved to tell stories, who wanted to make people feel something.

Looking back, it wasn't until I was broken down, in despair, stuck, afraid, hopeless, and desperate that I decided I had to make a change. I had to get back to myself because I felt lifeless, which is no way to live. However, getting back to myself was not something I knew how to do. At the time, I didn't even know that's what I needed.

I knew I needed to bring happiness back into my life, so I started by asking myself, when am I happiest. And it was on this road that I realized true joy and happiness is the excitement you feel as a child before people in the world take it out of you.

We must remember, though, that others are not to blame. We cannot blame others for living their lives in whatever way they know how, and when we cast blame on others, we give away our authority. You can always get back to that point of happiness and passion, and it is up to you and you alone. So I'll ask you again, who is your inner child; who is your original self?

Exercise Two
The Practice

For our next exercise, we are going to watch the life story of the child we visualized. You will come across moments along this timeline that may be acutely distressing. In those moments, take your time and remember you are an observer. You are not meant to relive these moments; rather, you are meant to see how they unfold. As much as you can, do not shy away from this pain. Honor it. Again, you may need more support to work through the harder moments along your timeline. Be kind to yourself, and ask for help if you need it.

Emotional healing is a lifetime affair. There is no need to rush through it or try to do it alone. The best outcome arises from your honest effort to face it, work through it, and understand that the behaviors of others have nothing to do with you; you are a bystander. Take a moment to prepare by closing your eyes, visualize the child you met during the first exercise, and feel them as separate from yourself. That child is from a different time and perhaps even a different world. Let's dive in.

Now that you have visualized this child and know who they are watch their life move forward. Imagine it as a movie playing out before you. Remember, you are the observer. Odds are—since you are reading this book—that somewhere along the line, this child experienced something that dimmed her inner light. To clarify, by inner light, I refer to the innocence, curiosity, love, and joy a child exhibits naturally.

Maybe one big event disrupted the child's life, or maybe it was multiple situations and people who brought the disruptions over time. Or perhaps this disruption happened while you are an adult. It didn't have to be a huge catastrophic event—it could have even been considered mundane—but the fact that it left an impression means it was important. Either way, we will look at these moments as lessons.

Watch this child as he goes from the beginning of his life, into the preschool years, through middle school, and into high school. Compare the child from the start of this timeline to the age of eighteen, then into the mid-twenties, to thirties, and so on. How has this person changed? What circumstances brought him to where they are now? What beliefs did this person form as a consequence of learning about the world?

The Lesson

As a child, you rarely understand that the things which happen to you don't happen to you at all. Read that again. The things that happen to you don't happen to you at all. Instead, they result from the *responses and actions of those around you.*

Growing up, children don't have autonomy or the ability to decide what happens in their life. If you are not taught to question the things that happen to you, you never will. You will take it for face value that it must be the truth.

Here we are offered a chance to decide *our own* truth. We do not have to live, think, or believe the way our parents did, or their parents, or their parents before them. What is considered true is often passed down through generations. It is up to us to pause, look at our lives critically, and decide if we want to keep living in the same manner.

Your timeline is a cognitive representation of the past, as well as the lessons presented as you formed your view of the world and of yourself. Understanding how certain events affected you presents the opportunity to move forward with or without the emotional pain of these lessons. You can choose to say *thank you*, accept the lesson, and leave the pain behind.

Take as much time as you need to watch the child's timeline. You can always come back to this exercise. Each time I repeat it, I uncover another hidden gem or piece of information that helps me further understand my beliefs and values. Each repetition helps me more fully understand the world which crafted me.

This concludes the second inner child exercise. If you repeatedly go back to one point along the timeline, dig in deeper and see if you can uncover why it is sticking with you now in this time of your life. Perhaps it is something you need to mourn, or maybe it is an instance you wish to have more of in your life. It could be many things, but give yourself the time necessary to process it so that you can allow it to be what it was—a moment in your life.

Once you can allow it to be just that, you can decide to either be free of it or instill it deeper into your life, whichever the lesson requires.

My Experience and Belief

Besides the tragic events which occurred throughout my life, something else that formed my belief system is how my peers and teachers treated me. I grew up in the woods, miles away from society. The nearest town had a population of 100 people.

While I grew up, I was lucky enough to have another family living with us once in a while, so I occasionally had other kids to play with. However, most of my childhood was spent by myself, especially in my younger years, when developing social skills is so important. This upbringing required that I learn how to interact with people differently than most. I also never learned that others might have different values and beliefs than mine.

My parents did an excellent job of teaching me to be kind and to love others. I was raised to be an open and trusting person, and living mostly separated from society led me to be sensitive to others. I was a tomboy whose knowledge was about the earth and life around me. I had such immense love for everyone that when they commented on my enormous feet, small chest, dirty clothes, and matted hair, I was deeply hurt and became self-conscious of my uniqueness.

Life went on as it always does, and now I can see where the insecurities about myself came from. Situations like this example continued throughout school and into my young adult life, where I found that being me was not socially acceptable. I am a bright, bubbly, happy person, but others labeled me a "dumb blonde," "bimbo," and "ditzy." Without realizing it, these words dug so deep into my psyche that I began to shape myself around what I thought others wanted. I spent my younger years desperately trying to fit in.

It wasn't until I was old enough to look back and question the behaviors of others and realize that I was never the problem. There was never anything wrong with me, and people will have their opinions whether I like it or not. Although my belief system and values were formed around these experiences, I now have the knowledge and ability to question and dismantle them. I can create new opinions and beliefs about the world around me that resonate with a life I love. After many years I can say with confidence that I am intelligent, beautiful, and creative. I no longer live in shame of my original, authentic self.

We have come to the beginning of a turning point. This is where you will decide what you want to do with the information and emotions you have uncovered through meeting your inner child and witnessing what they have lived through. You will start the next exercise by becoming a new part of the story; the hero or heroine, guardian, teacher, coach, or whatever feels right to you. You will step into each moment along this timeline and offer the support needed. You will be the support you need.

– Chapter 7 –

HEALING OUR TIMELINE

Exercise Three
The Practice

Go back to this child and follow along his or her timeline again. Except this time, instead of just observing, go to the child and teach her what she needs to know about the situation. Perhaps it is enough to offer her love and a safe harbor amongst the chaos. Be the person who you needed during these times. Don't just think about it; visualize it. If it helps, write her a letter.

Talk to this child and show her that innocence and love are things to hold on to and that she has done nothing wrong; she has failed no one. Others failed in guiding her to the knowledge and support she needed to make it out of the situation unscathed. Even the kindest, most selfless caregivers may not have given the support you needed.

They only know the world from their perspective; they can never know what you experience and what you feel.

You are your best teacher. You may not have had the proper support then, but you do now. And now you can undo the heartbreak.

The Lesson

The lesson here is that you are your best teacher because no one can ever understand what you are going through. No one. Not your mom. Not your dad. Or sister, brother, aunt, uncle, grandparent, or best friend. The beauty of this is that it allows you to forgive others where they may have failed you—or at least where you feel they have. It also helps you uncover the lesson which that part of your life taught you.

Remember, your experiences are lessons, and you are the teacher. So look at the life story of this inner child, see each experience for what it was, allow yourself to forgive, and let go of whatever hurt or judgment you are holding on to. Do this to help your inner child see the truth behind her experience, heal her relationship with herself, and heal her relationships with others.

My Experience and Beliefs

While moving across my inner child's timeline, I often came back to the same thing—death and solitude. At the time, it seemed I had no support. I felt forgotten and brushed aside. I felt abandoned when my parents stopped spending as much time with me, when my dad died and my mom left to live with her new boyfriend, and when the kids at school didn't show the same love for me as I had for them.

Eventually, the teachers, too, got tired of talking to ten-year-old me. I felt brushed aside when my brothers forced us to leave our home so they could sell it, and when we moved, my old friends forgot about me.

I felt forgotten when my mom and stepdad drank and fought at two in the morning on a school night, even after I begged them to stop so I could sleep. I became totally alone when my mom died, and I settled her estate with no help from my family. Yes, I spent much of my life having to do things alone.

Before I healed my inner child's heartbreaks, I told myself I was alone; no one was there for me, no one loved me, I didn't matter. I was no one. I was holding on to a lot of pain and resentment at this point in my life, and I had learned never to trust nor depend on anyone but myself. This caused a rift between me and anyone else in my life. My fear of abandonment prevented me from letting anyone in. Why should I trust anyone anyway?

Yet, this is no way to live. I believe that we are here on this earth, living life, to experience what it is like to be human and learn the complexities of human relationships —the complexity of love. I had so much love for these people who, in my mind, failed me. And it hurt to be left alone to live my darkest days by myself.

But in the end, you are all you have. This is not a bad thing, but as much as we love and extend ourselves to others, we need to remember that this life is ours and ours alone. No one else can dictate how we feel, think, learn, or act.

This is *your* life.

Do not give power to others by assuming that they owe you something for simply being your friend or family. They owe you nothing. This was a hard lesson that I had to learn. It is also something that many people dislike talking about. It is rather taboo to point out that the only person you need to rely on is yourself. It seems lonely and somehow lacking justice to the amazing social web we have built.

Truly, many gracious people exist in the world. It is also true that in the end, we must learn to ask for help and humbly rely on each other. But first, you must find your own inner strength. If you do not feel strong within yourself, you will always search for someone else, or something else, to provide that sense of strength and stability. You will be left feeling alone and angry with the world.

It is wonderful to be a part of a social web, where everyone depends on each other—each person giving and taking their fair share. Democratic society is founded on this idea. However, our childhood selves quickly learned that some people take more than they should, and some people give less than they should. As we grow, we get so caught up in what we think is fair; we forget our morality —that to be human is to be humane. Finding that sense of strength and stability within yourself makes it possible for you to be the one who does the right thing.

I had to overcome many hard trials by myself; does that mean I should sit and watch others struggle just because I did? Should I take more because I've struggled more? Should I give less just because I was given less?

It depends on who you ask, but I believe the answer is no. However, this wasn't always the case. Before I took the time to look at how my life experiences shaped me, I had become calloused and unforgiving. No one had time for me or my feelings, so I didn't have time for them.

But by looking over my timeline from an observer's perspective, I saw I had overcome a lot of tough situations; death and solitude were ongoing themes throughout my life, and that had turned me into a lonely soul. By realizing this, I found peace and stability in solitude. The solitude made me stronger. I survived; I did it by myself.

Not because no one was there for me or because no one loved me, as I once believed. But because this was my battle to fight. My road to walk. Looking back over my life and seeing that what I experienced involved no one other than myself brought internal peace and the ability to forgive others who were bystanders to my experiences.

Now I can move forward into a life that is filled with love and companionship because I know it is there, even if I don't see it at first. You, too, can find peace in your life story, but you must know the truth of your story first.

– Chapter 8 –

QUESTIONING OUR PERCEPTIONS

How do our experiences craft our perceptions, and how do our perceptions craft our beliefs? Before creating the life we want, we must first closely examine our beliefs. The life we live must be in alignment with our soul beliefs and values. The moment you cease questioning your perception and beliefs is when you close yourself off to any magic this world offers. Change brings growth, so we must be willing to change our perceptions and beliefs as needed. Staying open to multiple points of view expands knowledge and thinking because limits on what is possible are not set in stone.

How you inspect the world and how you perceive the world are different. Your life experiences have shown you how to view the surrounding environment, so when you inspect something, your experiences tell your brain your perception of it. You think without thinking. You have a unique way of viewing the world, and what you take away from that viewing can be shrouded in misconceptions and perceived opinions that you have formed from your experiences. Just as we need to reevaluate our biological response to threats, we need to examine our opinions and beliefs. The world is as it is, yet we all have our own views, beliefs, and opinions about what we see; this is our perception.

Questioning your perceptions, belief systems, and opinions is a humbling task. The older you get, the more you think you know, and your ability to take in new information and adapt as needed becomes limited. Are you uncomfortable with being wrong or admitting when you are wrong? How does the idea of questioning your perception sit with you? Can you allow change within yourself if it means letting go of your current beliefs and opinions?

Start from ground zero, and once you have released everything you think you know, then you can decide what pieces to keep. These pieces will be what is true for you and only you. It is not your job to push your perceptions about the world on others; they must come to their own conclusions. Do not take on the emotional and energetic weight of others' opinions. What is right for them doesn't have to be what's right for you, and from now on, you must live your life according to your authentic self. This is what you know beyond a doubt is true. This is your truth.

The only way to find it is to question everything that you think you know. Question your perceptions.

We have done the work of meeting our inner child and seeing our original selves, witnessing our life story, making peace with our lessons, and have become our own teacher. Let's take a moment to think about the last three exercises and reflect on how what we have done can change our lives.

Becoming aware of oneself is no small task. Hearing that voice in the back of your mind, feeling the pull of your soul to reach for more, is not something that everyone experiences. Some feel the pull of the soul but choose not to follow that call. Relish what you are doing, feel the essence of your mind, body, and soul shift to align with your vision of the life you want. Your original self is calling for you to bring her back, listen and trust in that calling. Move forward into your new life, one step at a time.

These exercises gave you a new perspective on your life and the lessons you have lived through. You took an objective look at how these experiences crafted your values and beliefs about the world. And now you can decide if these are beliefs you want to take with you into your new life. We will now go a little deeper to uncover how our perceptions and beliefs affect our lives—for better or worse.

As we develop during childhood, our brains form connections that help us make sense of the world. We are informed by how the external world responds to our words and actions; this is how we learn. However, as we move through life, the world begins to respond to our thoughts instead of our thoughts responding to the world. Read that again. As we get older, we cease responding to the world, and the world begins responding to us.

At least, that's what we think; this is where "the world is out to get me" mentality comes from. If you think the world is an awful place, then it will be. In reality, our brain responds to our *perception* of these stimuli and then continues to make connections and assumptions based on this perception.

The lessons we experience form our beliefs and help us decide what we value. Over time, we forget these experiences are why we have the beliefs and values that we do. We perceive the world and the actions of others in one way when the opposite could be just as true.

For example, if you believe you must climb the corporate ladder to be successful, you won't be successful until you reach the top—whatever top means to you. This is one perception based on a belief system around success. Much of the psychology behind this phenomenon is outside the scope of this book. However, let's just say that in order to change the world around you, you must change your perceptions. The best way to do this is to question them.

Exercise Four
The Practice

This fourth exercise asks you to explore and piece together where your beliefs and values came from. You can look at your belief system as your lens through which you see the world. This is where we form opinions of not only the world but of others and ourselves. We view the actions of others through our own belief system and then believe we know who that person is and what they stand for.

We spend most of our life making things up about the world. When we believe something about the world, then that is what we will see.

To start the exercise, let's begin with a couple of questions. How do you feel about the world around you? What lens are you using, and what experiences built your belief system that supports your lens? Who taught you how to view the world, and where did they get their information from? What is the foundation of this source of information? Is it reliable, or are you taking someone else's opinion for fact?

The Lesson

The lesson requires you to own up to the reality you've created. You think the world, so it is. You think the world is a cruel, unloving, and lonely place, so it is. You think the world is out to get you, so it is. This is the final thought I have for you. If you want to move forward into a life you love, one filled with your hopes and dreams, one that is meant for you and you alone, you must become a beacon of awareness, honesty, and integrity. The lies we tell ourselves spread like wildfire throughout our society. We are all connected. Break down the structure of what you think you know, as you will find that much of this was founded on lies and misinformation. Although it is not always nefarious, it is not your truth, and no one can speak your truth other than you.

As members of our glorious social web, we must honor our responsibility to spread awareness, honesty, and integrity. This begins with us questioning the very fabric of our reality—our perception—and to do so, we must go back to the beginning. Watch the movie of your childhood and ask yourself these questions.

Now you face a decision. Let go of these beliefs and move on, or suppress what you've learned, and continue fighting to ignore the fact that you can change your life but choose not to. You get to decide the world you live in. If you are truly ready to take control and create a life you love, you must part ways with the negativity that, through life experiences, has woven its way into your foundation. Do this, and you will make space in that foundation to fill with who you want to be, or the original version of yourself, your inner child.

My Experience and Beliefs

I experienced death and abandonment at a young age, which led me to believe that the world was a lonely place where no one cared about or wanted me. I have also lived with caregivers with severe anger management issues who would constantly lash out, acting as though everyone else around them was at fault or that no one could do anything right. This led me to believe I was never good enough.

Over time, I projected this belief system about myself onto those around me. No one could do anything right. I constantly held others to unrealistic standards, just as I had been.

Although I seldom lashed out at others for their perceived lack of common sense and inability to do anything right, I still held on to these sentiments, harboring negativity within myself. This behavior and attitude towards others were so far away from my authentic self and the person I wanted to be that I caused immense amounts of dissonance within myself.

I acted in ways that weren't true to my authentic nature, which played a huge part in my unhappiness. On occasion, I could be downright mean and hostile. Of course, early on, I was unaware of how and where this behavior rooted itself into my psyche and buried my soul.

I had to sit with the discomfort of it all and let myself feel the dissonance. I knew I was unhappy with my beliefs about others and my behavior because of my beliefs. I'd ask myself, *why do I do this*? I didn't like what I saw; it wasn't who I was or who I wanted to be.

From that point on, I began making connections between my thoughts and behaviors to my belief systems and from my belief systems to the external influences of my childhood. My belief systems and values were not my own but were created from what I witnessed before I could question the reality of what was going on around me.

Why do you think, feel, and act the way you do? Why do you make assumptions about others' behaviors? Who is feeding you the information you base your perceptions, beliefs, and values around? Why is it you dislike some people and not others? Everything we think is because of our own lens of perception, instilled in us from the time we were born. We had no say in our upbringing, and we often didn't have the awareness to question what we were taught, but we do now.

Conclusion

So, now that you've made it this far, what do you make of this book? Is it what you expected? You chose this book based on the title, cover, and description. Or maybe it was an inner calling. Maybe it was your soul's way of saying, "start here."

In the beginning of this book I told you I will share my number one tool for realizing your full potential in life. This tool is self-love. Everything begins to fall in to place when you love yourself wholeheartedly, but sometimes this also means doing things you don't want to do.

Yes, finding balance in our mind, body, and soul health is a lifelong affair. It is my hope that reading these pages has given you a sense of confidence and direction in creating a new life for yourself. If you want to change your life, all you must do is change your life. This takes dedication and discipline. If you want health and happiness, you must create it; no one else will do this for you. It is time for you to take the steps you know you need. If you needed a sign, this is it.

Illness of the mind, body, and soul comes from our own neglect. If you are not doing everything you can to better yourself and your life, you will never find what you are looking for. This is a heavier weight to bear for some but a drastic undertaking for all.

Now is your time.

Start with the health of your mind, your emotional self. Curate the stability and awareness that your unchecked nervous system is aching for. The interpretation of your surroundings and experiences is guided by this structure. It is an intermediary for your emotional self, the backbone for your physical self, and a blueprint of your energetic body. It seeks balance through peace.

Move into the health of your physical self to build strength and create movement. The health of your physical body is three-fold, requiring proper hydration, nutrition, and movement. Your life force can flow through you with ease, but you must allow it the tools and freedom within your body to do so.

Last and of utmost importance, your soul is calling to you. It is asking you for freedom from all the hurt, hate, and negativity that you have been holding on to throughout your life. Let go.

You read this book looking for the answer to where science meets the soul. You are the answer. You are where science meets the soul. Honoring the emotional, physical, and energetic versions of yourself allows for a fluid connection between survival and spirituality. Through practice and building healthy habits, you can overcome living to survive and start living a life true to your authentic self. You can live a truly soulful life.

Acknowledgments

I would like to give a special thank you to:

Self-PublishingSchool, for without your guidance this book would have not come to be.

Cutting-Edge-Studio.com for turning this book into a work of art, inside and out.

May I ask a favor?

Hello!
I do hope you enjoyed this book, or found it helpful in
your journey of becoming
your original self.

Being self-published, a lot of love, hard work, and
dedication went into creating
this work. However, without YOU it is all for nothing.

If you feel so inclined, please leave a review on Amazon
and tell the world about *Where Science Meets Soul*.

Truly, EVERY review helps.
Thank you kindly.

P.S. Don't forget to download your free Beginner's Guide
to Self Care at:
http://www.tandemhealth.online/freedownload

Made in the USA
Coppell, TX
20 July 2021

59225757R00066